LOCAL   COLLECTION.

AUTHOR	CLASS
JONES. P.P.	14

TITLE	No.

LANCASHIRE LADS AND LASSES.

Lancashire
Lads and Lasses

A Children's Companion of Folk Tales, Legends and
Traditions

by

Patricia P. Jones

Dalesman Books

1979

£1.15

The Dalesman Publishing Company Ltd.,
Clapham (via Lancaster), North Yorkshire

First published 1979

© Patricia P. Jones, 1979

ISBN: 0 85206 518 3

460554514

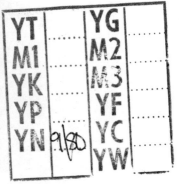

Printed by Herald Rusholmes Printers (Westminster Press Ltd.), York.

Contents

Cover design by Valerie Pye

Line drawings by the author

Introduction

LANCASHIRE is a county rich in legend, superstition, folk-lore and mythical stories. We have only to mention Pendle Hill and we imagine those weird, wild witches who ended their days, after the notorious witch trials, at Lancaster Castle and passed into the fiery flames of folk-lore. All towns and villages at one time possessed their own ducking stool. This was a contraption of justice made to decide the fate of a suspected witch. Unfortunately it was in constant use. Witch hunting was once a national sport and many innocent, ancient old ladies lost their lives, as at the Lancaster trials, on the evidence of children and hysterical adults.

We know of the old Lancashire industrial towns such as Bolton where the folk dressed for Sunday wearing their now famous clogs. We cannot think of Lancashire without a mention of the clog. It brought a new way of life to the community, giving rise to various new pastimes and games. This innovation saw the birth of a dance, the clog dance, and the folk took great pleasure in devising intricate and unique steps to out-dance their rivals. Whole villages organised clog dancing competitions and it was a great honour to represent your village as a dancer.

Such distractions brought light and welcome relief from the hard, tedious labours of reality. Folk worked long, tiring hours and this included the children too. There was little cause for merriment. The community's hub of social activity would be centred round the church; people gathered there in storm and sunshine and thanked their God for his small mercies. They thanked him for the safe gathering of the harvest; for the rebirth of life. Many of these services were in existence long before the arrival of christianity, but had to be incorporated into the new faith to please the people, for such customs die hard, if at all.

Lancashire has had her share of heroes, men of stout heart, who defy the passage of time. Soldiers of fortune such as we associate with the Blundells of Ince, kingmakers such as the house of Stanley, her men of medicine, of religion, of politics. We must also remember the ordinary men made great by the whims of circumstance. Such men as Oliver Atherton of Aughton, a martyr for the rights of the common man, and Billy Boats, a slave trader who was found as a baby in a boat of reeds floating down the Mersey. Such men as Arthur Douglas, a sailor who turned out to be a lady in disguise mourning the loss of a lover by seeking adventure amidst the roar of guns and the swoosh of the flying sails.

Remember too the giant at Speke who was wined and dined by a great king, and did you know that Lancashire was named after Sir Lancelot of the Lake to whom it was once given from King Arthur?

But Lancashire was a wild, lonely stretch of land, inaccessible and remote. A land of dark shadows, cold, biting winds and will o' the wisps. Travellers were few, scarcely daring to wander the dangerous peasant paths. Dangerous for these marshy moorlands and murky bogs became the haunts of highway men, rogues of ill repute who, in swirling capes and mounted on rearing horses, mocked law and order. As a direct result of Lancashire's inhospitality as a county, it became isolated and did not progress as well or as intellectually as the rest of Great Britain. It could not be influenced by infiltrating fashions from the continent of Europe; it adhered strongly to the old faith and suffered much in consequence. It also retained its traditions, customs and way of life longer than anywhere else in the country.

What makes us superstitious—who can say? The roots of superstition began many thousands of years ago with the advent of civilisation as we know it today. Perhaps superstition is a series of events, trials and errors in that infant past from which a lesson was learnt and passed on to the surviving race of man. Such lessons would become law, then in time would be distorted as so quickly happens, leaving us with exaggerated versions of stories which in themselves become unbelievable. I believe, however, that there is an element of truth in all stories of fantasy, but the origin of the story has long since gone to the shadowy grave with its proper instigator. What is truth and what is myth?—the poetic licence of writers and storytellers is notorious, and so matters must remain with the skilful analysis of the historian. He must work as if he were opening up a gift, stripping away the outer trappings of ribbon and pretty paper to discover the secret of the contents within. Strip away the fire from the mouth, the steam from the nose of the dragon and we might have an ordinary animal of large proportions that struck terror into the dwellers of its domain. It could have existed perhaps, but not in the elaborate and fantastic form in which it has been portrayed. Yet because of these very distortions we choose not to believe in its existence at all. Perhaps it was the parent of our present day Loch Ness monster, if indeed we believe in that. But who can prove the non-existence of this beast?

We are a curious race, we like to hear tales of great deeds and daring; we like to hear of battles fought against the odds when good overcomes evil and we create gods out of ordinary people. Such folk heroes as Robin Hood, Peter Pan and Dick Turpin bear this out. We exaggerate and we glamourise our legends, a process which lends itself to gross misrepresentations with only a flicker of the truth remaining. Herein lies its charm. Characters become larger than life, old wives' tales become accepted truth and can govern a community's way of life.

The old way of life produced many traditions and customs. Services were held and festivals created relating to the seasons for the weather was of utmost importance to survival. It was imperative to be able to understand the weather signs; to be able to determine forthcoming rain or drought and to adapt accordingly. Living in the lap of nature made the senses more receptive and the people more aware of the hardships to be endured.

Animals, we know, have their own in-built senses governing such things and much was made of this by our forefathers. Numerous superstitions concern animals and animal behaviour. Animal superstitions fall into the realms of the fantastic, sometimes mocking our well-educated common sense. Such a tale is that of Dildrum, king of all cats. Try to remember that somewhere within the story lies the grain of truth, the original story. See if you can spot it and forgive the exaggerations that give it charm and character and bring the story to life. Enjoy the story of Dildrum, accept it for what it is, believe it if you dare and enjoy all the other tales of the fantastic, of adventure, of romance that you will find waiting for you in the pages that follow.

Pots and Pans

POTS AND PANS was the name given to a small hill that overlooked the village of Saddleworth. Its strange and unusual appearance lent itself to romantic legend. Scattered all around the hill were huge boulders and mysteriously shaped stones. No-one knew their origins but some believed a sect of Druids had once worshipped their gods on the hill and that the stones had been used in their ceremonies. Other, more superstitious folk, had another theory. It must be admitted that this was no ordinary hill but one steeped in mystery. The local villagers thought it to be a little enchanted, a little magical and the home of goblins, fairies and elves. It is important that we believe in such things for therein lies our story.

Once, long ago, when monstrous animals roamed the earth and all men were giants, two giants lived on two hilltops. One hill was known as 'The Height of Greenfield', the other as 'Pots and Pans'. The giants were good friends and often played a game called 'casting the stones'. They would pick up huge boulders (as ordinary boys picked up stones) and hurl them, crashing, into the valley below. One of these original stones, with the

marks of giant fingers imprinted on its hard surface, was believed to have been thrown as far as Ashton-under-Lyme. This friendship, however, was not to last.

Rimmon was a beautiful maiden, living in an enchanted dell known as Rimmon Pits, with whom the giants fell madly in love. Rimmon chose between the two and this caused bitter conflict. The rejected giant challenged the other to mortal combat. During the ensuing fight the chosen giant was killed and Rimmon, in her anguish, committed suicide. Nymphs who dwelt in a nearby fountain carried the bodies and laid them to rest somewhere on The Height of Greenfield.

It was believed until recently that water taken from a font on Pots and Pans contained special healing powers.

Pots and Pans

Near to Saddleworth village square
Behind the smithy snugly stood
A hill

And banefully the wind's breath blew
Around her chasms dark, a flood
So chill

The village folk in fear agreed
That goblins lived there and fairy gnomes
To cry

On lonesome nights in moonshine moaning
Far from firesides and mother's homes
A sigh

It swept the hilltop, made grass a swirling sea
Curled round corners, its surging, frantic flight
A dance

And I, blinking, stood a charmed and awesomed figure
Strained to catch the tale, stretched my full height
As in a trance

Long ago the soft winds whisper
When men were giants in this land
Of old

Two strong giants, Alphin and Alder
Lived, on each his hill, lordly, grand
And bold

Now Alphin was fair, a gentle, game giant
His hill, The Height of Greenfield, was known
By name

9

But Alder was older and darker and sober
He lived on a hill, Pots and Pans, quite alone
The village folk claim

The giants played the long days as if brothers
Casting huge stones to the valley below
The earth raged

Shaking the ground with their coarse, racous laughter
Bemused laymen actors, the world's greatest show
Ever staged

Thus the two passed the long, lengthy summers
Followed autumn, drab winter and spring's
Showery rain

Then into their lives fell a sad, sinister shadow
A whispering, pale effigy that brings
Only shame

Rimmon, they say, was a beautiful maiden
Who lived at the end of an enchanted dell
Fathoms long

Attended by fairies, the little folk's gentry
You'll hear if you listen by the old wishing well
A song

The giants are in love, both in love with the maiden
Who lives with the fairies in an enchanted dell
But which one will win her, this magical maiden
For whom will we hear the chime of the bell

Rimmon chose Alphin, the fair and the gentle
To wear the young damsel's bright ring
Of gold

So Alder, in anger, called Alphin to combat
Challenged his right, his wounds sore from the sting
And cold

Two days and nights the earth raged to their music
Scattering boulders and small rocks by the score
To and fro

From one hill to the other with exact precision
But on the third day Alphin could throw no more
It happened so

That Alphin was struck with a fatal collision
He died on the instant leaving Rimmon to grieve
At his side

But she, in her sorrow, killed herself quickly
And followed her lover, a saintly reprieve
The two died

It is thought that the nymphs who dwelt in the fountain
Tenderly bore our two folk heroes homeward
As one

Somewhere on The Height of Greenfield they lie sleeping
Fast as the solicitous shadows that ne're chanced
The sun

And Alder was lonely as he spoke to the bleak plains
Forever bereaved on his hill in the clouds
To repent

The blow that in anger deprived him of friendship
His life sadly meaningless as the days came
And went

In Saddleworth village a rumour maintains
That Pots and Pans plays magical tricks
And can heal

By splashing its silvery waters in faith
Pilgrims in sickness came hobbling on sticks
In earnest appeal

Our story remains in the keep of the fountain
Where goblins remember the battle of kings
In torment

Where Rimmon the beautiful Fairy Queen maiden
Sits by these waters and constantly sings
A lament.

The Strange Tale of Dildrum

PROBABLY the strangest story to come from Lancashire was one told about Dildrum, a local tom cat. Dildrum belonged to a blacksmith and his wife and they all lived together in a tiny cottage on the edge of a forest. The blacksmith was so good at his job that he was constantly over-worked. His wife, being a good wife, always had his supper ready and his slippers by the fire.

On one such night the blacksmith returned late, ate his supper and then began to nod, wearily to sleep. He was rudely awakened by a large, black cat that shot down the chimney and yelled, 'Tell Dildrum, Doldrum's dead'. In the same instant the cat disappeared back up the chimney. The blacksmith thought he had been dreaming but was doubly astonished when his own cat screetched, 'Did you say Doldrum was dead?' Dildrum also disappeared up the chimney and was never seen again. When the story reached the ears of the villagers everyone began to wonder what had happened to the missing cat. Many folk put forward their own stories

but the accepted one went like this:

Doldrum had been king of the cats and Dildrum had been next in the royal line. Suddenly the old cat had died and that then left Dildrum as king of all cats. He had left the small cottage and the blacksmith to sit on a golden throne in the kingdom of cats and so became the most wealthy cat in the land.

The Strange Tale of Dildrum

Have you heard down forest paths
The whisper of a tale

Have you seen the scarecrow laugh
Blowing in the gale

Have you touched the snow wind's wrath
Along some hedgehog trail

As in the shadows skulking, something silent sat
The probability it will be, Dildrum, called king cat

Have you heard the gamesman's song
Lilting in the wood

Who pricked the ears of rabbits long
And wore a gamesman's hood

Whose magic tale is told erelong
In distant choppers' thud

Whilst in the shadows skulking something, silent sat
The probability it will be, Dildrum, called king cat

A cottage stood by forest pines
Silent in its sleep

Here Dildrum lived between the vines
The willows and the sheep

Besides the blacksmith's grain sacks fine
Safe in the blacksmith's keep

As in the shadows skulking, something, silent sat
The probability it will be, Dildrum, called king cat

The blacksmith's work was never done
His laboured hours spent

With farriers' tools, his race hard won
The horse-shoe, skilful, bent

But when shadows they outpaced the sun
The blacksmith homeward went

And in the shadows skulking something, silent sat
The probability it will be, Dildrum, called king cat

13

The blacksmith's wife, she made him tea
The blacksmith smoked his pipe

Beside the fire they sat all three
The quiet, homely type

But such is life's game levity
Tis something fairy like

For in the shadows skulking something, silent cat
The probability it will be, Dildrum, called king cat

Outside a storm in rage it blew
Disturbed the blacksmith's nodding head

A large, black cat shot down the flue
And this is what it said

In tones of nervous accents true
Tell Dildrum Doldrum's dead

And in the shadows skulking something, silent sat
The probability it will be, Dildrum, called king cat

The blacksmith sat in mute surprise
Could not believe his ears

Such nonsense surely must belie
The judgement of the years

Cats cannot talk has been the cry
To do so would be queer

And in the shadows skulking something, silent cat
The probability it will be, Dildrum, called king cat

Up Dildrum sprang in sudden haste
As if in trance he cried

Did you say Doldrum's dead, and then he raced
With agile, cat-like stride

He left the cottage as if he chased
The black cat, now his guide

As in the shadows skulking something, silent sat
The probability it will be, Dildrum, called king cat
Dildrum was never seen again

The village folk recall
Each to a story soon laid claim
And told what did befall

The village shouted Dildrum's name
As the greatest cat of all

Whilst in the shadows skulking something, silent sat
The probability it will be, Dildrum, called king cat

Some say that Doldrum had been king
The feline aristocrat

But on his death his golden ring
And throne on which he sat

To Dildrum passed in offering
Who now became king cat

And in the shadows skulking something, silent sat
The probability it will be, Dildrum, called king cat

Have you heard down forest paths
The whisper of a tale?

It tells of the most wealthy cat
Who dines on shrimps and snails

It makes the blacksmith proudly laugh
As he works his tongs and nails

And in the shadows skulking something, silent sat
The probability it will be, Dildrum, called king cat.

Riding the Stang

I THINK we have probably all heard the story about the cruel husband who continually beat his unfortunate wife. The shy, devoted wife would stay at home all day washing and scrubbing and darning his socks, she'd cook his meals but he would stay out late with his friends, get drunk and then return home to mistreat her. It is a sad story and, in some cases, true. There is a similar story told in Lancashire but with a slight difference.

Down by the blacksmiths there stood a row of cottages and in the end cottage lived Sam Potter and his wife, Martha. Sam was a collier by trade, a huge, sturdy, six foot giant of a man. Martha, on the other hand, was only five foot tall, was very slim with a sharp, pointed nose and tongue to match. Such noise and shouting went on behind those walls that some-days the vicar could hear it up at his church which stood on a hill at the other end of town. The townsfolk worried about little Martha for Sam was so strong and they'd wait, never daring to interfere, and hope she had come to no harm. When the noise and shouting stopped Sam always strode through the cottage door and headed for the Blue Boar where he'd sit, drinking merrily, without a word about his wife. One night Clem White, the shoe-maker, decided to hide in Sam's parlour and wait for the collier to come home.

He and Josh Jones crept, unseen, the following day, into the Potters' parlour. At about eight o'clock that night Sam came home. Martha brought him his dinner which he was quick to eat and all went quiet. Clem thought it was a wasted journey but, suddenly, the cottage came to life amidst loud shoutings and bangings. The two stayed hidden until the noise became unbearable; then, determined to show Sam up for the cowardly woman beater they thought him to be, they rushed forth into the room to denounce him.

The scene before them was much as expected—pots and pans flew through the air and the shouts proved quite deafening. They were so overcome by the utter chaos that it took several minutes before they realised exactly what it was they saw. Martha, every inch of her five foot strained with the action of lifting a wooden stool, loomed over the bulky form of Sam who lay crouched in a corner of the room. Martha threw cups and saucers and kicked mercilessly at her husband. It was some time before either of the couple spotted the intruders staring out of the parlour. On their discovery, however, Martha became even more angry

16

and began shouting and throwing things at them as well. Clem and Josh quickly left followed by Sam and they didn't stop until they reached the safety of the Blue Boar. Clem and Josh reproached Sam for allowing Martha to beat him and it soon provided quite a local scandal.

'I don't mind,' replied Sam, 'it pleases her and it don't hurt me.'

That was the cause of the Riding the Stang. When a wife beats her husband, instead of it being the other way round, all the neighbours put a small boy on a stang or pole and carry him through the streets where the beating has taken place. Every now and then they stop and the boy recites a verse to the accompaniment of pots and pans and kettles struck by the crowd. The verse of the song would be as follows:—

> Ting tong to the sign o' the pan
> She has beat her good man
> It was neither for boiled nor roast
> But she up with her fist an'
> Knocked down mesther post.

Riding The Stang

In Lancashire they ride the stang
On certain days in certain towns
With pots and pans the people bang
And act like jolly circus clowns

Up and down the streets they go
Singing songs and silly rhymes
Letting all the people know
Of certain ladies' shameful crimes

Now and then they stop and shout
To passers-by along the way
And so the scandal is let out
And gossip mongers have their say

That lady there beats her old man
And he a giant, six foot tall
Ting tong to the sound o' the pan
Come and listen one and all

Every night you'd hear her yell
To the sound of crashing cups and spoons
And no-one knew just what befell
Her good man in those closed rooms

But now it's out the townsfolk cheer
Ting tong to the sound o' the pan
She must face the taunt and jeer
Because she beats her old man

In Lancashire they ride the stang
On certain days in certain towns
With pots and pans the people bang
And act like jolly circus clowns.

Speke Hall

HOUSES do not consist of brick and mortar alone but also reflect something of the people and families who live within their walls. This is especially true of the larger manor houses such as that at Speke, lying seven miles from the centre of Liverpool, and overlooking the river Mersey. Throughout her colourful history she has housed men of learning and of politics, soldiers of fortune, ladies of tragedy and men of violence; a multitude of family intrigues weaving and delicately forming the pattern and atmosphere of this charming black and white country manor house.

The first record of a house at Speke can be found in the Domesday survey of 1086 where it is described as the manor of Spec, one of several properties owned by Uctred. By 1170 the ownership had passed to the Master Foresters of Lancashire. It was next owned by Roger Gerneth but in 1372 was passed, in marriage, by Annota, heiress of Benedict Gernot, to Adam Molyneux. Eventually, in 1524, it became the property of William Norreys. Perhaps the most colourful of all the tenants, Nor-

reys produced nineteen children and added several features of architectural interest to the hall. He was succeeded by his son in 1568. His great grandson, also named William, was a staunch royalist who fought for Charles against the parliamentary forces. In 1650 parliament seized Speke hall and its estates. The last of the male heirs was Richard Norreys who died in 1731 and the estate was conveyed by his niece, Mary Norreys, to Lord Sidney Beauclerc. Latterly the hall was owned by the Watt family and was given to the National Trust in August 1942.

In the courtyard at the hall, two yew trees grow side by side and have been romantically named Adam and Eve. They are believed to be four hundred years old and are of immense and moving beauty, especially in autumn.

Speke Hall

In garments of green the foresters came
The masters, the masters, their manor to claim
And who can deny them and who can them blame
As she stood in a wood by the river

Black and white, plaster and wood
Shelters the gentle, the bad and the good

Her timber walls black, her plaster sides white
And out of yon forest there rode a bold knight
Sir William de Norreys came seeking a wife
And he courted her down by the river

Black and white, plaster and wood
Shelters the gentle, the bad and the good

Sir William was married with much speed and haste
And granted the manor and Speke hall estate
And his young wife was gentle and so fair of face
As the silver moon shone on the river

Black and white, plaster and wood
Shelters the gentle, the bad and the good

Twelve years it had passed and twelve years they had seen
Now William's fine family it numbered nineteen
And their gay laughter echoed through the woodlands so green
And was heard on the banks of the river

Black and white, plaster and wood
Shelters the gentle, the bad and the good

The king in his castle sent William a plea
Go fight off the Scots for your king and country
And take your fine sons and do honour for me
And leave your sweet banks of the Mersey

Black and white , plaster and wood
Shelters the gentle, the bad and the good
So went de Norreys his sons by his side
There on Flodden field, well some of the died
But all are remembered and sung of with pride
Back home on the banks of the river

Black and white, plaster and wood
Shelters the gentle, the bad and the good

Two hundred years onward and the hall it stands bare
It's Lord Sidney Beauclerc who is master of her

And they call him a tyrant but he's not one to care
For the chill that blows up from the river

Black and white, plaster and wood
Shelters the gentle, the bad and the good

Lord Sidney's wife, Mary, was meek and so mild
She spent her days weeping for the fate of her child
And sad was the house where the sun never smiled
And the shadows cast lots on the river

Black and white, plaster and wood
Shelters the gentle, the bad and the good

The rain it did fall and the wind it did blow
Her baby she threw to the cold moat below
Then she drank of a potion and she drank it so slow
And she died on the banks of the river

Black and white, plaster and wood
Shelters the gentle, the bad and the good

I stood in the courtyard and saw the tall trees
In summer, spring, winter and autumn's brown leaves
And as I remember my gentle heart grieves
For the house on the banks of the river

Black and white, plaster and wood
Shelters the gentle, the bad and the good

Local Fairs and Shows

NO English town or village is complete during the summer months without its annual show or garden fete. The scene is one of hustle, bustle and colourful pageantry. During the month of May we crown our May Queen, during the month of July we crown our Rose Queen, and their gay and splendid trains parade through our local streets. All our towns celebrate summer with these shows, although their content and purpose have changed somewhat over the years.

Shows such as these are, in fact, remnants of traditions that have remained with us through the passage of time. Formerly they were held to commemorate various ceremonies dedicated to the seasons. Today we still preserve our Harvest Festivals and our 'Bringing in the May'. To 'Bring in the May' a king and queen, wearing wreaths of flowers, were followed by the youth and maidens of the village dressed as followers or mummers bearing garlands and were attended by a band of music. A bough of hawthorn covered with blossom was carried as a sign of the coming summer. As the procession passed through the village the streets were strewn with flowers and the mummers sang and danced, receiving for their reward cakes, ale and wine given by the housewives.

Local Fairs and Shows

Summertime is coming in
Sweet marigolds lift their sleepy heads
To watch the frivolous hours begin
And days can know no rest

Again the scented breeze is here
To linger on night's calm abode
And bid adieu to seasons more severe
He answers summer's song

Each flower head bursts its clammy cell
Stands bunched along the border line
In rows, the busy humming bee can tell
Where the pollen grows

And on the green the village ponies graze
With donkeys and white, flapping tents
For the annual show with colour all ablaze
Is ready to begin

The heavy horses with ribbons in their hair
Parade before the crowded stands
As mothers holding children, stand and stare
And fall to remembering

Now the Household cavalry appear
To excite the younger boys and men
Who dream of guns and know no fear
The whole summer long

The cattle bellow in their lowly pens
Amuse the few who venture there
Black and white, fine specimens
Of local breeders' pride

The judges of the dogs and cats
Congregate and raise a knowing brow
Whilst parachute jumps and acrobats
Thrill the growing crowd

The strawberry stall sells its tarts
To eager, podgy hands outstretched
Elegant trotting ponies pull their carts
The Punch and Judy show begins

The morning ends with the horse and hounds
And farmers in gay attire blowing horns
That are often heard on the open downs
Between the fox and men

Now coffee flasks replace the weary tread
As idle chatter pursues its common course
The old folk dine on ham and bread
And wait, patiently, in chairs

Soon the sound of morris men is heard
Clasping sticks, they perform their dance
And twirl and skip as one, then paired
Complete with hobby horse

Now is the turn of Jock to show his skill
As every sheep is guided to its goal
And so the sheepdog from a lonely hill
Enjoys his master's praise

The jumping horses follow in the ring
In readiness to chance the big, brush fence
To clear with agile cat-like spring
The water and the bank

Lengthy shadows now pursue their course
Chill winds replace the warming sun
The rider unsaddles his big, brown horse
And people pull on woollen shawls

The great finale when evening calls
With flashing lights from the fireworks display
Lighting wide-eyed faces, the deserted stalls
For the show's swan song has now been sung.

The Grey Man of the Wood

KING Henry VI was beaten at the Battle of Hexham in 1463 but was successfully conveyed into the county of Lancashire and hidden for twelve months. He was, eventually, betrayed by Thomas Talbot, his cousin John and Sir Oliver Tempest. An alliance had been made between Tempest and the Talbots and, in order to save their estates, they gave the king up. At this time Waddington Hall belonged to the Tempests; they inherited it through their ancestor, Sir Roger, who had married Alice, daughter of Walter de Waddington, in the reign of Edward I. Sir Oliver Tempest, his wife Joan and daughter, Elizabeth, were now in residence.

In 1464 a group of labourers returned through the forest glades that skirted the broad and beautiful Ribble below Waddow. Through the arches of the wood they saw an object, just visible, and this gave rise to strange stories of demons guarding lost treasure, of a secret mine once worked in those parts and to the grey men of the wood.

Gregory was a round-chested, long-armed hunchback who worked for the Tempests at Waddington hall. He was particularly fond of Elizabeth Tempest and was always at her beck and call. During the year of 1464 she engaged Gregory, unknown to her father, as a messenger commuting between herself and a strange hobgoblin who lived below ground in a secret cave. Gregory was eventually apprehended in the wood by Sir

Oliver and, in order to save himself from hanging, betrayed his mistress, revealing the entire story.

Sir Oliver sent his own message to the hobgoblin, inviting him and his friend to dinner at Waddington hall. The invitation was accepted and the hobgoblin and the grey man of the wood, being the king and his servant in disguise, were surprised at dinner and taken prisoners. King Henry was sent to London where he was sentenced and condemned to death. Before he died he predicted of the Talbot family that for nine generations in succession they would conceive one wise man and one weak man by turns, after which the name would be lost.

The Grey Man of the Wood

A battle raged at Hexham in fourteen sixty three
The muskets roared and thundered
To the shout of King Henry

The royal army faltered and so it lost the day
But through the smoke of shot and shell
The king was got away

To Lancashire, in hiding, they kept him for a year
The loyal friends and gentlemen
To whom his life was dear

In Waddow by the Ribble in fourteen sixty four
Strange stories were abounding
Of daemons by the score

Deamons who lived underground in secret mines of gold
And frightened lonely travellers
Or so the tale was told

They wandered in the forest dressed in cloaks of grey
Guardians of some devil's gold
The villagers would say

Gregory was a hunchback with round, projecting chest
His arms were long and ape-like
In life he had one quest

He was a greedy hunchback who dreamed a splendid dream
Of owning lands and castles
And to wed a fairy queen

The fairest maiden in the land, Elizabeth was her name
And when e'er the maiden called
The hunchback quickly came

Elizabeth Tempest, lady grand, lived at Waddington hall
Her father was Sir Oliver
A knight on constant call

Elizabeth, late one evening, into the garden crept
Unknown to all at Waddington
Who, in their beds, now slept

A message gave to Gregory, a letter to convey
In haste and utter secrecy
She showed her man the way

Take the near path quickly, into the distant wood
Turn right beside the pasture
Where the old fir tree once stood

Walk carefully through the bushes to the sharp edge of the rock
Your path will then be thwarted
For a large oak tree will block

The entrance you are seeking but do not stand in fear
Hold tight the tree and whistle thrice
And all will then 'come clear

The hunchback did her bidding and on the whistle thrice
He fell into an eerie cave
The home of rats and mice

As Gregory sat in terror afraid to even breathe
He met an old hobgoblin
The ugliest dwarf he'd ever seen

Who took the message gruffly, in his grey eyes were hate
As he vanished to the darker depths
He bade the hunchback wait

Gregory in the darkness a story did recall
His mother told him long ago
That somewhere at the hall

A subterranean passage led to the Ribble's bank
Used by the grey man of the mine
And how his heart, it sank

For coming down the passage the ugly dwarf returned
Now only for his freedom
The hunchback sorely yearned

Gregory was escorted out of the dreaded place
And with another message
To Elizabeth made haste

The answer is, my lady, they be snug and so secure
As the fox in hole at hunting
'Till they hear from you once more

Elizabeth used the hunchback as carrier to and fro
Of messages and food stuffs
To the hobgoblin's cave below

Gregory thought the goblin was a guardian of the gold
And though he loathed each visit
His reward would prove two-fold

His mistress would inherit the treasure of the cave
Then Gregory would be rich and so
No more to toil and slave

Thus said Gregory, 'I must wait and bide my time
For ladies sometimes married serfs
Such a treasure could be mine'

It happened on one moonlight night, a figure in a hood
Came creeping at the midnight hour
Caught the hunchback by the wood

The stranger was Sir Oliver to whom the story was relayed
Gregory saved himself from hanging
For his mistress he betrayed

Sir Oliver bade the hunchback a message to convey
To bring the goblin and his friend
To Waddington next day

Sir Oliver sent another to Thomas Talbot with the cry
To come at once to Waddington
As quick as horse could fly

Sir Oliver had promised a prize of high degree
A king, no less, in hiding
Their prisoner soon would be

Went Gregory to hobgoblin, bade him fetch his master fine
To Waddington the morrow
As welcome guests to dine

Then came the king and servant dressed in cloaks of grey
To dine as guests invited
At Waddington next day

The servant's name was Madoc, a suspicious man who thought
The invitation was a trap
And feared the king be caught

As they sat a-dining a whistle it was heard
'Fly, my lord,' cried Madoc
For the king's life must be spared

Out through a secret passage the king in anguish fled
Escaped into the lower fields
And to the forest sped

He crossed the river Ribble by Bungerly Hippingstones
And came to Christian Pightle
A land of Elfish homes

Henry hid in Clitherwood, closely hunted by the pack
Led by Sir Oliver and his friends
Who quickly brought him back

The king was sent to London astride a chestnut mare
His feet tied to the stirrups
And how the folk did stare

To Thomas Talbot's family it's said the king did speak
Nine generations you will bare
One wise man and one man weak

And so a royal sovereign suffered much that day
Tortured and dishonoured
With his life he had to pay

The Simnel Cake

MOTHERING Sunday, also known as Simnel Sunday, is a familiar date in our calendar, a day when the young members of a family visit their mothers with some small gift. Today we would probably take her chocolates or a bunch of flowers but at one time this gift consisted of a cake. This cake was known as Simnels and was eaten on Mid-lent or, as we know it, Mothering Sunday. Simnels was named after a likable couple called Simon and Nelly who, due to a domestic quarrel, first baked this delicious cake.

Our ancestors believed that cakes baked at this time of the year had magical powers. They thought that by eating Simnels, or, as we call them, hot-cross-buns, it would protect their house from fire.

The Simnel Cake

Simon and Nelly were husband and wife
Who lived in a village a plain, rural life
They brought up their children of fourteen or more
To furrow the field and scrub the stone floor
Then the children all married and left their first home

And built their own houses of bricks and of stone
And built their own fires and baked their own dough
And tilled their own fields and watched their wheat grow

For Simon and Nelly the days seemed so long
Without the gay chatter, the patter of song
The rooms seemed lonely, the table looked bare
Without the sweet laughter of children there

The season of Lent was now drawing near
Said Nelly to Simon, 'I have an idea,
Let's celebrate Easter with the children all home
It would be so sad to spend Easter alone'

The children accepted this re-union at Lent
But now Nelly saw problems to such an event
Plenty of food would be needed to fill
The extra mouths, and so, a large bill

Nelly had to be thrifty, they hadn't much wealth
And, peeping into her pantry, she found on the shelf
Some unleavened dough, the basis of a cake
Which she quickly began to prepare for the bake

Simon agreed, 'The cake sounds most fine,
But what about this idea of mine
Let's use the remains of the Christmas plum pud
As its centre, you know, it should taste good'

It was agreed and all went as planned
Nelly prepared the cake for her oven, grand
Her pride and joy, but to her dismay
Simond said, 'Let's cook the cake another way'

It should be boiled Simon stubbornly insisted
Nelly said, 'Cakes are baked,' but Simon persisted
The argument flourished as words led to blows
And so a small matter, unreasonably grows

Nelly flung a wooden stool across the tiny room
Simon, in his anger, chased Nelly with the broom
Nelly grabbed the rolling pin, her honour to defend
Simon smashed a dozen eggs and they called the fight to end

It was concluded finally that the cake in question be
First boiled, then baked, to end all controversy
The wooden stool provided fuel for the oven and the pot
The eggs coated the outside and so provide that familiar shine it's got

The cake became known as the Simon and Nell
Bnt soon it was shortened to simply Simnel
And on Mothering Sunday during Lent of the year
We all eat a Simnel cake with hearty good cheer.

Arthur Douglas

DURING the eighteenth century many young girls and women joined the army and navy as soldiers and sailors. They would fight side by side with the men without being suspected until some unlucky accident or severe wound revealed their well kept secret.

In the Liverpool records we learn of just such a person, calling herself Arthur Douglas, who signed aboard the ship *Resolution* and carried out all the duties appertaining to a landsman. The report read as follows: 'A young person, five feet high, aged about nineteen, signed aboard the ship, *Resolution*, with Captain Barber, under the name of Arthur Douglas, proceeded with the ship, carried out all respective duties, went aloft to furl the sails, was frequently mustered amongst the marines when they exercised their small arms and, in short, carried out all the duties of a landsman, was discovered on Saturday last to be a woman by one of her messmates.'

It is said that he found out her sex on the passage and that she, to prevent discovery, gave her word to keep him company when next they came to port. On their arrival in port, however, she refused his advances. The officers in general gave her a modest character and said that by her

behaviour she must have had a genteel education. The only information the captain managed to find out about her was that she left home on account of a breach of promise by her lover.

Arthur Douglas

In Liverpool town there lived a maid, a maid of high degree
And she loved a lad of some renown but a false young man was he
T'me fol dol diddle, t'me fol dol day
T'me fol dol diddle dum day

In Liverpool town one May morning, one May morning so rare
This maid to the church did go but her true love was not there
T'me fol dol diddle, t'me fol dol day
T'me fol dol diddle dum day

In great despair this fair young maid changed her clothes and name
From silks and such to a manly dress she sailed the raging main
T'me fol dol diddle, t'me fol dol day
T'me fol dol diddle dum day

She signed aboard a likely ship when she was just nineteen
As Arthur Douglas she was known and sailed the raging main
T'me fol dol diddle, t'me fol dol day
T'me fol dol diddle dum day

There came a lad, a strapping lad, and her secret soon did see
Don't tell, don't tell, the young girl cried, keep silence sir with me
T'me fol dol diddle, t'me fol dol day
T'me fol dol diddle dum day

I'll not tell the sailor said if you promise me sincere
To wear my ring when next we port and say you'll be my dear
T'me fol dol diddle, t'me fol dol day
T'me fol dol diddle dum day

I'll wear your ring the maiden said, I'll wear it night and day
And the sailor kept her secret till they harboured in the bay
T'me fol dol diddle, t'me fol dol day
T'me fol dol diddle dum day

But once ashore the young maid cried, no I'll not marry you
She quickly left and bade farewell to the sailor dressed in blue
T'me fol dol diddle, t'me fol dol day
T'me fol dol diddle dum day

Come all you roving sailors take heed from what you've heard
Be wise, my boys, be wise and don't trust to a young maid's word
T'me fol dol diddle, t'me fol dol day
T'me fol dol diddle dum day.

All About Sunday

SUNDAY has always been considered a very special day, not only in Lancashire, but throughout the country. It is so special that no-one is expected to go to work and everyone sits down to a special lunch at midday. Some people will not drink on a Sunday and, in some families, it is not considered respectable to play such games as rugby or football. Times, however, are changing and rules are constantly being broken because, generally, public opinion is not so strict. The observance of Sunday as a special day is sadly disappearing but before it does let us try to remember how it used to be.

Sunday has always been celebrated as a day of rest. The reason for this is concerned with a legend about St. Paul and the Archangel Michael, who were once sent by the Lord to see how the souls fared in hell. Michael showed the horrified apostle all the terrors of Hell; souls distressed by every form of torment and torture, agonised souls hanging on trees, a firey oven with seven flames, a well of fire guarded by twelve demons like unto kings, the sea of Hell with seven waves and full of strange monsters. These sights made the messengers of the Lord weep and St. Paul asked the Lord to allow the wicked rest in Hell every Sunday until the day of doom. The Lord granted St. Paul's request and so Sunday has become known as a day of rest.

Part of the traditional English Sunday must include Sunday School, that quaint innovation essential for a respectable childhood. It usually meant dressing up in our very best clothes and sitting on a wooden stool in a big hall with several other children. We were told interesting stories about Jonah and the whale and Noah and his ark. Tiny text cards containing a passage from the Bible were given out at the end of each lesson and kept to form vast collections.

Sunday School, when it first came into being, was an immediate success in Lancashire, especially in Oldham, Bolton and Manchester, and had a huge following. Every girl and boy wanted to join in the classes but this was not always possible because, during the early days of the movement, teachers had to be paid for their trouble.

In 1785 the Wesleyan Methodists of Oldham decided to establish a Sunday School but were worried about the cost of doing so. A Mr. Samuel Scholes of Higher Moor, Oldham, made a sensible suggestion. If the Methodists were to establish a school without much expense, Mr.

Scholes advised, then they must supply the teachers themselves from within their congregation and each member must give as much time as possible. This advice led to the foundation of the school at the old chapel, Bent Brow, Oldham. The Sunday School, as we know it, had come into being.

For many years Sunday was the only day of rest and, contrary to Victorian and present times, was the only day suitable for recreation. Sunday was quite often chosen for the performing of mystery and miracle plays. The mystery plays were dramatic representations of biblical histories, whilst miracle plays were founded on legends of the powers of the saints of the church of Rome. The distinction between the two was not always observed. The church was soon found to be inconvenient for the staging of such plays and so a stage was erected in the open air. Different plays were selected for performance by the various traders. The painters and glaziers performed the herald angels appearing to the shepherds, the butchers told the story of the temptation and the bakers set forth the last supper.

Amongst all but the higher classes Sunday was the chief time for festivities. The wedding feasts or 'bride ales' were always held on this day. The morris dancers could be seen dancing in the village streets accompanied by jingling bells, and often joined the congregation in the church dressed in their gay attire.

But the most enjoyable Sunday tradition must be the eating of the midday lunch. This was an elaborate meal usually consisting of a leg of lamb or pork, salted, seasoned and roasted for a couple of hours in a hot oven. It would be stuffed and served with three veg., Yorkshire pudding, roast potatoes and either mint or apple sauce. This would be followed by either apple pie and fresh cream, jam roll and custard, blackberry jelly and sauce or any other local delicacy.

This may sound quite a substantial meal but, on reading an old menu belonging to a noble family who lived in the Preston area of Lancashire, and who had the honour of entertaining King James I to Sunday lunch, I begin to wonder. When James I in 1617, on his return from Scotland, passed through Lancashire, there was every desire to do him honour and give him a hearty welcome. He was well dined as the menu to follow would suggest:

Sunday's Dinner, 17th August, for The Lord's Table

First Course

pullets—boiled capon—mutton boiled—boiled chickens—shoulder of mutton roast—ducks boiled—loin of veal roast—haunch of venison roast—burred capon—pasty of venison hot—roast turkey—veal burred—swan roast—chicken pie hot—goose roasted—rabbits cold—jiggits of snipe pie—mutton boiled—breast of veal boiled—capons roast—beef roast—tongue pie cold—sprod boiled—herons roast—curlew pie cold—mince pie hot—custards—pig roast.

Second Course

hot pheasant (one)—quails (six for the King)—partridge—poults—artichoke pie—chickens—curlews roast—peas buttered—rabbits—duck—plovers—red deer pie—pig burred—hot herons roast—lamb roast—gammon of bacon—piegeons roast—made dish—chicken burred—pear tart—pullets grease—dryed tongues—turkey pie—pheasant pie—pheasant tart—hogs' cheeks dried—turkey chics cold.

The dinner was then followed at about 4 o'clock by the rush bearing which was preceded by piping and performed by the village folk.

Seats were not provided in churches until the 15th century and the floors of the church, being flagged, made the feet of the worshippers very cold. The richer members of the community brought their own cushions but this was not possible for the poorer folk. Rushes were found to be ideal and also provided warmth inside the church. The custom of taking these rushes to church developed into a religious festival. As the custom became more of a festival the rushes were ornamented and bourne by young men and women dressed gayly and bearing flowers to decorate the church.

The rushes were cut from the marsh and made up into long bundles, dressed in fine linen, silk ribbons, etc., and flowers. The rushes were formed into the shape of a hay stack and a gay procession of people with music, drums, ringing of bells and other such demonstrations attended the rush cart to church. The party entered the church at the west end and set down their burdens, stripping them of their ornaments but leaving the heads decked with flowers, cut paper, etc. The company then returned to the village and spent the rest of the day in dancing and merriment.

Stepping Out On Sunday

Dressed for Sunday in my best
Red cord coat and woollen vest
Little girl upon a quest
Stepping out on Sunday

Mother's pride and mother's joy
Giggling girl, sniggering boy
A little lost, a little coy
Stepping out on Sunday

Sitting on a wooden stool
Six and seven at Sunday school
Who will help me play the fool
Stepping out on Sunday

Jonah and the mighty whale
Noah's Ark that once did sail
To save the spider and the snail
Stepping out on Sunday

But then it seems that all too soon
The village clock is striking noon
We sing our last religious tune
Stepping out on Sunday

By the common, by the stream
Where the grass is tall and green
The morris men are heard and seen
Stepping out on Sunday

Jingles jangle on the air
In the village, by the square
You will see the actors there
Stepping out on Sunday

All dressed up in costumes gay
Easter, Whit and Christmas day
Performing now their mystery play
Stepping out on Sunday

Down the stairs the children go
Happy as the shadows grow
Chatting now in voices low
Stepping out on Sunday

The fire's burning strong and bright
The candles lit to give us light
As we go laughing through the night
Stepping out on Sunday.

Souling

PETER PIPER lived in the little village of Woodholme and was known to the villagers as a souler or 'sowler'. He was a member of a small group of 'sowlers'. Peter and his friends would gather in the village square on the eve of All Souls Day, during the season of Lent, to perform the old religious custom of souling. The custom had been in existence for so long that nobody actually knew the connection between it and the Church.

The Roman Catholic Church pray for the souls of the dead on All Souls Day. It may have happened that the poorer folk said to their rich neighbours, 'Give us cakes that we may feast today and fast tomorrow, and pray for the souls of your forefathers and ours'. So it came to be that All Souls Day was celebrated throughout the country.

Peter Piper and his friends, after gathering in the village square, then went around the village, stopping at all the houses of the well-to-do and, standing in a group, sang this song:

> A soul cake, a soul cake,
> I prithee, good missus, a soul cake
> One for Peter, one for Paul
> And one for him who made us all
> A soul cake, a soul cake.

The group would then remove their caps and wait for the lady of the house to give them the cakes she had baked in order that the poor folk could celebrate the feast. If the lady of the house were a mean person and her family were a mean, selfish family, the singers sang another song that went like this:

> An apple or a pear or cherry
> Or owt as'll make us all merry
> Up wi' th' kettles an' down wi' th' pon
> Gi' us good ale an' we'll be gone.

The singers would, once again, wait for the appearance of the lady of the house and, if she still did not come forth, they sang yet another song now lowering their demands. It went like this:

> If you ha' ner a penny a hawpenny'll do
> Gi' us a cake or an apple or two.

There is a similar rhyme still sung in Liverpool but this is in connection with carol singing at Christmas. The Liverpool two line rhyme was as follows:

If you haven't a sixpence a halfpence will do
If you haven't a halfpence then God bless you.

Once again we have a custom directly connected with the Church and religion, the verses of which are familiar to us, having been used as parts of other songs and traditions. This poetic licence is used throughout the history of folk-lore and certain lines and verses keep re-appearing. This is particularly true with the history of folksong and ballads. It makes the history of traditions a little confusing at times, and sometimes—although we may never know the particular custom—we may know the song connected with it very well.

Souling

Mathew went a souling
On all saints day

Went out in the morning
And the horse did neigh

Mathew saw a rich man
Dressed in red

Then he saw a poor man
Who shook his head

The first man was a tailor
In silken dress

The second was a hawker
Quite penniless

Prithee sir a soul cake
Mathew said

To the gentle rich man
Dressed in red

Prithee sir a soul cake
An apple or a pear

To give up to the hawker lad
Standing over there

I do not have a soul cake
The rich man cried

I do not have an apple sir
Nor a pear beside

I only have my wares sir
My coat and my hat

To wrap up in the winter months
And you're welcome sir to that

Now Mathew and the hawker lad
For the tailor they would pray

And clothed all in the tailor's coat
The hawker went his way

Mathew went home smiling
On all saints day

The lowly sheep where sleeping
And the horse did neigh

The stars where in the heavens
Twinkling starry bright

And the candles stand a burning
On this all saints night.

Billy Boats

LIVERPOOL and her many colourful characters have given rise to numerous stories and legends of fame, fortune and wealth, all closely connected with great families such as the Rathbones. Billy Boats is just such a story.

Billy Boats was an orphan found in a basket floating down the river Mersey, was rescued and placed in the care of the Blue Coat School, an institution that trained young boys for a naval career. They called him Billy because it was a popular name at that time and Boats was to remind him of his first home. He graduated from this school to take up a post on his first ship, and his progress was such that he soon became captain of his own vessel. He sailed this ship all over the world, amassing a small fortune until he was able to buy his own fleet of ships.

With the coming of the years a new and far more rewarding merchandise was becoming popular, that of slave trading. Billy Boats became a slave trader. It was not a pleasant occupation but it was profitable and he made a quick fortune. The slave trade, buying and selling African natives as cheap labour, was a universal fever and many family fortunes were made in Liverpool at this time. Cruelty towards the slaves was quite common and they endured much hardship and suffering, many dying after a couple of years in our country. Billy Boats was a hard man but he was not cruel and he did much to help the position of the slaves in our country. Because of this the slaves respected him and his reputation spread throughout the town as a man of considerable influence.

The peak of Billy Boats' success came one day as one of his many ships sailed into port. It was laden with gold, jewels and silver taken from a Spanish vessel. It sealed his fortune as a millionaire. He was so overcome with joy that he ran through the streets of Liverpool shouting, 'born a beggar, die a lord,' which, in fact, he did.

He is buried in Liverpool and an entry still exists under his assumed name of Billy Boats. The man remains a mystery; we will never know where he came from or his true identity. His relatives, on his death, emigrated to America, destined forever to be known as 'Boats' and never knowing their real family name.

Billy Boats

There was a sea captain called Billy Boats
Born a beggar, die a lord
Commanded a slave ship round the African coasts
Born a beggar, die a lord

Now Billy Boats' true name will never be known
Born a beggar, die a lord
Found in a boat, a waif with no home
Born a beggar, die a lord

He was sent to the Blue Coat to learn and to school
Born a beggar, die a lord
And like many before him, proved he was no fool
Born a beggar, die a lord

Commanded a slave ship with honour and skill
Born a beggar, die a lord
Got many a stern slaver to bend to his will
Born a beggar, die a lord

Come down to the Customs House by the old dock
Born a beggar, die a lord
You can purchase a black girl plus collar and lock
Born a beggar, die a lord

As Billy Boats sailed from Annamaboo
Born a beggar, die a lord
He had sixty slaves and a good hearty crew
Born a beggar, die a lord

42

He brought them all safe into Liverpool town
Born a beggar, die a lord
At a coffee house sold them fifty gold crowns
Born a beggar, die a lord

Now Billy Boats' lodgings were down Drury lane
Born a beggar, die a lord
As a slaver and merchant he'd honour and fame
Born a beggar, die a lord

But now his old sea bones lie in the cold earth
Born a beggar, die a lord
And only King Neptune remembers his worth
Born a beggar, die a lord.

The Clog

DURING the industrial revolution, with its growth of cotton and weaving towns, a new type of shoe became popular in Bolton which gave Lancashire one of its most famous assets. It was the clog.

The clog first appeared in Bolton with the arrival of some Flemish weavers who wore a French and Dutch peasantry shoe called the sabot. The local Bolton weavers and country folk did not wear shoes at this time or, if they did, wore shoes of untanned leather very much like the mochassin worn by the American Indian. This new type of shoe, although superior to the local type, was too weak to stand up to the rougher conditions in Lancashire. The sabots had been designed for use on flat, sandy tracks. The Bolton weavers solved this problem by adding iron to the soles of the shoes and this type became known as the Lancashire clog.

Some clogs, however, were still without iron and these were known as 'barefoot' clogs. They were the cheapest and most simple of all the clogs and were only worn by the women and the young girls. Pit clogs were worn by the colliers. The iron on the pit clog was very stout, the sole being two inches in thickness and generally studded all round with brass head nails. Dancing clogs were thin and light with a slight curve from heel to toe. The leather uppers were stamped with every type of pattern and had fancy decorations along the edge of the sole which were of bright nails. Dancing clogs were always bought one size smaller than normal to give a close fit. Duck-bills were the most commonly worn clogs, and the more lavishly decorated syles were nick-named 'coorting clogs' or, as in Colne, 'dandy clogs'.

There was much rivalry between the young dancers as to who was the most skilful. Each dancer added a difficult step to his own dance in an effort to become the best dancer in his neighbourhood. One dancer in Accrington could dance on an 18-inch square plate of glass. The grandfather of a Bacup coconut dancer could dance with a jug of water balanced on his head. In order to obtain an audience the clog dancers joined the ranks of other performers such as singers, musicians and novelty artists. This produced a spirit of competition between them and so helped to raise the standard of the dancing.

The only unfortunate point about the clog was not to do with the shoe itself but with the use the Bolton boys discovered for it. They began to use the clog as a deadly weapon with which to fight their battles. Known as 'up and down' fighting, it was a most brutal method of settling quarrels. Both men had a right to kick their opponent on any part of the body with their clogs and were also allowed to squeeze the throat. At races and fairs, contests of this kind attracted big crowds. The men wore heavy wooden clogs covered with iron plates and studded with large nails. Death often resulted from such contests which were legally banned during the reign of George IV, the punishment for such fights being a branding on the hand for the offenders.

The Clog

The sabot, the sabot
Was once a habit
Not a rabbit
The sabot

The clog, the clog
Was made from a log
Not a bog
The clog

The shoe, the shoe
Carried them through
Not a gnu
The shoe

The stud, the stud
Made them look good
Not like mud
The stud

Duck-bill, duck-bill
Worn by Tom and Phil
Not a pill
Duck-bill

Up and down, up and down
Fighting in Bolton town
Not a clown
Up and down

The dance, the dance
Hop, skip, prance
Not in France
This dance

The clog, the clog
Was made from a log
Not a bog
The clog.

Animal Superstitions

ANIMALS have lived closely with man for as long as civilisation has existed and probably even longer. It is not surprising then that numerous legends and superstitions have arisen concerning most creatures. It would take a complete book in itself to name them all and so here I will mention only two or three and perhaps tell you of the others another time in another book.

Have you ever heard an old man or woman say 'the cat is raising the wind' and wondered just what they meant? It seems our ancestors noticed every peculiarity of their animals and formed theories to explain them. When a cat tore at the cushions or carpets with its claws it was considered to be a sign of wind. Presumably they thought that by its actions of clawing the cat caused the wind to blow. However the probability of this lends itself more to the imagination than to reality.

Have you watched a cat as he sits snugly by the fire busily washing his face? This action in itself may mean very little to us except to say that here we have a very clean cat. The ritual of the cat washing its face had a much greater significance to our great grandparents. If the cat drew its paw completely over its forehead it was considered to be a sign of good weather; if it did not, then it betokened rain. I wonder how many house-wives watched anxiously on washing day to see if the family cat, by washing its face, would foretell the good weather or the bad.

Cats, at one time, were considered unhealthy companions and much was believed about their connection with any outbreak of sickness in the family to which they belonged. Cats were said to 'draw your breath away', and young mothers would panic if one approached the pram in which their babies slept. This was a natural fear for cats have a habit of seeking out a cosy corner in which to curl up and baby's pram or cot could make an ideal bed. The baby itself would not be able to push the cat off the pram and, as a consequence, would suffocate. This then led to the understanding that cats 'draw your breath away'.

Playing for any length of time with a cat was thought to keep a person in constant ill health. The only explanation I can find for this theory is that certain people are allergic to the cat, the components of the fur having an adverse effect on the metabolisms of the body and causing an un-uncomfortable swelling or an unpleasant rash. Some illnesses could then be the result of an association with a cat but most of the accusation is mere supposition borne through a general rustic ignorance.

From the familarity of the cat we move to another most popular domestic animal, the dog. He too has become the centre of some curious and interesting superstitions. There is no greater link in the animal world than between man and dog, a situation nurtured through tolerance and understanding, a successful cohabitation of necessity and charity. It is certainly true that in some cases an unbelievable bond can grow between a man and his dog. Whether this relationship is anything other than one established on affection I cannot say, but some people believe such a bond to extend beyond life to continue in the realms of the spirit world. So great can be the attachment of a dog for his master that when the master is sick the dog will sit and howl outside the door of the sick room. If the dog is driven away by anxious relatives and returns as many times, it is considered a certain indication of the master's death.

In relation to this existing bond of man and dog, it has been noticed that on the death of the master, the dog sometimes dies very soon afterwards. I have known an instance when this very situation occurred: the old man died and was quickly followed by his white terrier dog who, I was assured, suffered a broken heart. Linked with this idea that dogs are acquanited with the spirit world is the belief that they can foresee the future. When a dog begins to whine it is considered to predict calamity in one form or another. I think the explanation here probably lies in the animal's extraordinary 'sixth' sense which, when found in people, we like to label as intuition.

Birds, also, were most popular subjects of our superstitious folk lore. A jackdaw was always an unwelcome visitor, particularly when it perched on the window sill of a sick room for this was a sign of coming death. I have heard it said that the same calamity follows if a small bird flies directly into a window pane. The belief is that the person who witnesses this accident will, themselves, fall ill and die or someone dear to them will meet with such fatality. A white pigeon at a sick room window, however, has a double meaning. It can be the messenger of death, the piegon being the representation of an angel come to guide the departing soul to heaven, or it can bear the good news of a complete recovery. It seems to be a case of close your eyes and hope for the best! Here we have a charming superstition which, ironically, contradicts itself and, by so doing, cannot ever be wrong in its predictions.

Swallows seem shrouded in superstition and, even today in a world of concrete and noise, they are a much respected bird. If they, or martins, built their nests in a barn or house, it brought good luck to the owners. If, for any reason, they foresook their haunts it would betoken misfortune. This superstition might seem unlikely to exist in our modern, progressive age, but I know people who, year in and year out, suffer the mess and inconvenience of these birds rather than risk the possibility of losing their good luck and inviting misfortune. The swallow is a fortunate bird for he is pampered and protected, every effort being made to attract him back to his old nesting grounds.

Another such protected bird was the robin. The farmers believed that, by killing a robin, their cows would give blood instead of milk. They even made up a rhyme about it, so serious was the business of superstition:

> A cock Robin and a Jenny Wren
> Are God almighty's cock and hen
> A Spink and Sparrow
> Are the Devil's bow and arrow.

We cannot conclude without the mention of the magpie. Most of us can probably recite the verses about this bird and will know that one sighted on its own is an evil omen. Typical of our ancestors, they were careful enough to produce a remedy that would break the evil charm. In this case the custom was to raise the hat in salutation or, if you were a lady, to curtsy; another was to cross the breast and another to cross the thumbs. For the various sayings connected with this bird we must turn to the verses of the popular nursery rhyme. The Lancashire version was as follows:

> One for anger
> Two for mirth
> Three for a wedding
> Four for a brith
> Five for rich
> Six for poor
> Seven for a witch
> I can tell you no more.

In conclusion, perhaps the emergence of our animal superstitions will give us an insight into the importance between the relationship of man and beast. Perhaps, also, we may acquire a greater understanding of our own pets for, I feel, there must be an element of truth in the roots of all our beliefs.

Animal Superstitions

Watch that cat, watch that cat, our mother used to say
And if it climbs on Molly's pram, shoo that cat away

Kick that dog, kick that dog, send him from our door
The old man now is surely dead, we'll see that dog no more

Swallow, swallow in the sky, catching wind and rain
Build your nest up in our roof and please come back again

Robin, robin don't you fret perched on rustic gate
The farmer will not harm you, nor will he harm your mate

Magpies, magpies in the field over by the wood
One's for evil but there's two and so our fortune's good

Jackdaw, jackdaw cawing loud what troubles you today
The sun is up, the world's a-new and so be off I say.

Treacle Dipping in Southport

I HAVE just discovered an exciting game that was most popular in the Southport area of Lancashire. Any number of people could take part and it helped if you were quite fond of treacle. It was known locally as treacle dipping.

All you need to play is a slightly raised platform in the centre of the room on which you place a table and, on the table, a dish. Into this dish you must pour a quantity of treacle until it is about three to four inches in depth. Now you must throw into the dish some coins such as a two-penny piece, which will later provide the prizes for the successful players. According to the rules these coins can only be removed from the dish by the teeth of the contestants. You will also need a large supply of feathers, the reason for which will become apparent later.

Having set up your table on the raised platform with the dish of treacle, the next step is to assemble the contestants in a line. Each player must stand on the platform in turn so that everyone in the audience has a clear view of the proceedings. The person on the platform must now fold his arms behind his back and attempt to remove the coins from the bowl. As you can imagine the faces of the contestants would reappear covered in the sticky mass of treacle—and this is when the real fun starts. The audience, who have been given a handful of feathers, rub them into the

faces of the players. The feathers, of course, stick to the treacle leaving the unfortunate contestants looking like misplaced ostriches.

Treacle dipping, however, is a very messy game and should only be played when supervised, otherwise it could end in disorder with a lot of cleaning up to do afterwards.

Treacle Enough To Spare

Once when our friend Anna Jayne
Had a birthday at her house
We all went round and played a game
After we had eaten cheese and scouse
And she had shown us her pet mouse
And it had run through Molly's hair

There's treacle for you and treacle for me
And treacle enough to spare

Then Anna Jayne's mother appeared in view
With a bowl held under her arm
Yelling, children this is what you do
And she had a sixpence in her palm
Which she threw in the bowl and to our alarm
It was placed on a table by a chair

There's treacle for you and treacle for me
And treacle enough to spare

Next came Anna Jayne's father, proud
Poured some treacle into the bowl
He clapped his hands and said aloud
Now to this end must be your goal
To win the sixpence from the treacle bowl
To use the hands will be judged unfair

There's treacle for you and treacle for me
And treacle enough to spare

But before the game could yet begin
We all held feathers in our hand
This was followed by an awful din
For we were led to understand
We stuck the feathers, that sounded grand
On someone's face, full fair and square

There's treacle for you and treacle for me
And treacle enough to spare

51

Everyone waited expectant and hushed
Then up stepped Jennifer Green
She dipped in the bowl looking ever so flushed
And when she emerged, well you should have seen
She had treacle where her face should have been
Then we stuck the feathers to her nose and hair

There's treacle for you and treacle for me
And treacle enough to spare

But Jennifer missed the sixpence and so
Up stepped Jack o' the hill
Everyone counted one, two, go
We watched Jack ducking, it was such a thrill
And the treacle would swish and the treacle would spill
'Till it covered the table and chair

There's treacle for you and treacle for me
And treacle enough to spare

Jack was unlucky, that's what he said
So up stepped Bernie the brain
Into the bowl he stuck his head
We didn't think we would see him again
He nearly succeeded, it was such a shame
For he looked so full of despair

There's treacle for you and treacle for me
And treacle enough to spare

Next came Martha followed by Paul
Robert and Andrew and Kate
Wendy and Peter and that's not all
Yes everyone shared the same fate
There was Harold and Tim, he's my best mate
And Sandra the pretty, the fair

There's treacle for you and treacle for me
And treacle enough to spare

Last of all up stepped I
Anxious to have my go
And feeling rather silly and shy
How I did it I don't know
But up came the sixpence, shining so
That everyone stopped to stare

There's treacle for you and treacle for me
And treacle enough to spare.

It was a good party, that.

Jingles and Games

AS I went out walking in the village of Aintree, near Liverpool, I passed an infants' school and heard a chorus of voices creeping through the open windows and escaping on the frosty morning air. I thought the song familiar and remembered singing it as a child. It brought back pleasant memories of a happy, carefree childhood. A flood of such songs invaded my thoughts and, pausing, I smiled, wishing myself back some twenty or so years. I remembered many old skipping songs and circle games such as Hop-scotch, Blackthorn and Ring o' Roses. The song the children had been singing was a favourite and most popular game played amongst girls. Called a ring or circle game, one girl stood in the centre of a circle of girls and she was supposed to be the mother. She began the game by singing the following verse:

> Here comes a man who wants a wife,
> Who wants a wife, who wants a wife
> Who will he choose to be his wife,
> Out of all my lovely daughters?

All the girls then chanted a reply giving details of how they would behave as the perfect housewife. The different chores such as washing, ironing and sewing were always acted out with much enthusiasm. The chant was usually a four line verse listing all the domestic duties imaginable and, where possible, they added to this list. Girls everywhere added to the song and so no one version would be exactly the same. After the girl in the centre had sung her verse, the others followed with their verses:

> This is the way we wash the clothes,
> Wash the clothes, wash the clothes,
> This is the way we wash the clothes,
> All in the early morning.

This would be followed by the rest of the verses:

> This is the way we wring the clothes,
> Wring the clothes, wring the clothes,
> This is the way we wring the clothes,
> All in the early morning.

> This is the way we iron the clothes, etc.

> This is the way we knead the dough, etc.

53

Because the girls added so many different jobs and tasks the length of
the song was variable. The game ended when the ideas ran out, and then
the mother of the group would sing this verse:

> Here stands a man who wants a wife,
> Wants a wife, wants a wife,
> Which will he choose to be his wife,
> Choose one, choose two, choose my fairest daughter.

The girl in the centre then chose another girl from the circle who
became the new 'mother' and the game began again.

Blackthorn was a game played mainly in the Blackburn and Colne
areas of Lancashire. It was originally played only by girls but there can
be no strict rules in children's games and boys were sometimes included.
Blackthorn was a fairly simple game played by any number of children
at one time. A long line of children gathered on one side of a lane or
street and one child remained on the other side. The group of children
were supposed to represent sheep and would begin to shout:

> Blackthorn,
> Buttermilk and barleycorn,
> How many sheep have you today?
> More than you can catch and fly away.

The children then scattered far apart and ran across the lane, the object being to reach the other side without being caught by the lone child who represented Blackthorn. The group crossed back and forth until only one person remained to be caught and then that person became the unlucky Blackthorn.

It is also interesting to remember the many nursery rhymes and jingles that could be heard in any playground in Lancashire. Some will be familiar, others perhaps not:

> Friday night is my delight
> And so is Sat'day morning
> Sunday noon it comes too soon
> And so does Monday morning.

> There's owd Tom an' young Tom
> An' young Tom's son
> Young Tom'll be owd Tom
> When owd Tom's done.

> Owd Jim Grundy went to the fair
> He bowt four horses an' one were a mare
> One were a black'un an' another couldn't see
> An' one had its yed were its tail should be.

> Owd Brown's cow
> Had a wooden leg
> An' everytime he milked her
> He hung it on a peg.

> There was a little man
> He had a little gun
> An' o'er yon field he run, run, run
> He's a white straw hat
> A belly full o' fat
> An' a pancake stuck to his bum, bum, bum.

> What's yer name
> Mary Jane
> Where d'yer live
> Down the grid
> What number
> Cucumber
> What house
> Pig scouse.

> Arf a leg, arf a leg, arf a leg of mutton
> Into the pan of scouse rolled the six onions.

> Them that buys beef, buys bones
> Them that buys land, buys stones
> Them that buys eggs, buys shells
> Them that buys ale, buys nowt else.

The Parish of Aughton

IT IS safe to assume that a church has existed at Aughton for a thousand years or more, the discovery of the Saxon cross dating from the reign of King Alfred the Great lending substance to such a claim. The antiquity of the church and its architecture is paramount, the very essence of its foundations oozing with the throb of regenerating peoples, weaving a pathway through the winding, narrow roads and culminating at the gates of St. Michael's. Here then must I seek out the old stories, the habits and the customs of a bygone Aughton, here in the midst of the tall, majestic walls of its ancient parish church I will pursue my journey through the avenues of her long and silent past.

Among the many fixtures at St. Michael's we find the ever popular, ever celebrated, sanctimonious angels of which there are twelve. They are affectionately and collectively described as 'The Twelve Old Ladies of Aughton'. It seems appropriate then that my first story should have some connection with the old ladies for, unlikely as it may seem, in 1785 the twelve angels of Aughton acquired a goddess.

One sunny summer's day in 1785 a dusty and dishevelled tramp arrived in the parish. His name is recorded as Graham and he was typical of the sundry travellers found upon the road at this time. His profession was fashionably known as a quack, a peddler in remedies and quick cures. Graham was adamant that he had discovered a salve, a magic elixir, a secret knowledge for the attainment of health, beauty and longevity. This great discovery, this most marvellous gift, he now brought with him for the benefit of the people of Aughton. Graham did not come alone, however, for he also brought with him a goddess of beauty, a vision of loveliness, whom he called Vestina. These two most unusual figures would bury themselves up to their necks in the earth and from this position Graham would entice the amazed onlookers to do the same. The idea, he explained, was to cover the body with good, British mud; this ensured such a beauty as enjoyed by Vestina, such soundness of health and such longevity of life as they had never known. It is not recorded whether the people of Aughton took this advice or not but it certainly caused a stir within the small community. Indeed, Vestina became acknowledged locally as the patron saint of beauty specialists and mixed bathing. For a short time anyway the twelve old ladies of Aughton had their very own. goddess.

Now Aughton may have had her own goddess but did you know she also lays claim to her very own martyr? I suspect that the name Oliver Atherton means very little to anyone now, in fact we would probably be excused for neglecting its notoriety. But a great deal was said about Oliver and a great fuss was made over his poor corpse before it finally came to rest in his own orchard, believed to be somewhere in Burscough.

It transpires that Oliver had certain convictions that contravened the laws of the land. In short he refused to pay his tithes, a position with which we are not probably wholly unsympathetic. Such tithes were made payable to the lay rector of Ormskirk who, at this time, was the Countess of Derby. Unfortunately such defiance, beit justified or otherwise, could not go unpunished and so the Countess of Derby was obliged to have Oliver conveyed to prison. Conditions in the prisons were deplorable, proving ideal breeding grounds for disease. Oliver, on serving two years of his sentence, died. Oliver's friends, also residents of Aughton, managed, through various devious means, to acquire the corpse of the lately deceased. These men, together with the corpse, travelled the length and breadth of Lancashire, embarking on a grand tour. As they arrived in each town they left poor Oliver's body at the market place by the cross as a spectacle of injustice to the serving man. To the market cross itself they pinned a notice:

> Here lies Oliver Atherton of Aughton
> and of the parish of Ormskirk who,
> by the Countess of Derby, has been
> persecuted to death for keeping a
> good conscience towards God and
> Christ, in not paying of tithes
> to her.

Yet another colourful character to follow the road to St. Michael's was a young lady called Ann Monk. Her profession, we learn, was that of singer and we find her, surprisingly, in the pay of the parish. She was given £1 10s. to sing for a year. Her board and lodgings were paid for by the parish and, during her stay in Aughton, she resided at the Stanley Arms. The accounts at the Stanley Arms state: '43 dinners for Ann Monk—singer—28 shillings'. How times change! We may speculate as to the type of song Ann was accustomed to singing, be it the music hall of Dolly Gray or the more reserved monotones of the parish drawing rooms but, whatever, I feel sure she brought a little happiness and a pleasant interlude into the lives of the congregation.

Certainly, at this period in her history, Aughton was considered a very go ahead place indeed. We discover that the local men were paid the grand sum of 2s. 6d. to kill a fox, that Aughton had its own ducking stool (a most bizarre form of justice, albeit a spectacular one) and, most interesting of all, that Aughton, in 1787, possessed one of the first umbrellas ever seen in England. This celebrated umbrella was an unspoilt luxury of leather and whalebone which cost the community the exorbitant sum of 14 shillings. It played a significant role in the successful administration of the funeral service during bad weather. The umbrella was not, in any way, related to those ardent followers of ladies' fashion, but was purchased for the sole purpose of keeping the bald headed clergymen dry on such occasions.

During the 1600s and 1700s the parish employed a local man in the official capacity of dog whipper. His annual wage came to 10 shillings and he was considered a most important member of the community. It appears that, at this time, everybody took their dogs to church, resulting in the most ludicrous pandemonium and chaos. The preacher's job, I imagine, was not enviable. One dog would take a dislike to another and a fight would develop. At this point the dog whipper would intervene, equipped with a whip and a large pronged, pincer-like contraption to catch and separate the quarrelsome dogs. The prevailing commotion would start the other dogs barking and the scene must have presented quite a spectacle, hardly conducive to what we recognise as a respectable, normal and harmonious service.

If people had unusual habits they were also very superstitious, folk medicine, witchcraft and the making of magic potions playing a major role in their everyday lives. Tales of the supernatural were rife and stories of hauntings and ghostly apparitions were numerous. Aughton was no exception and she lays claim to at least two ghostly stories.

The first of these stories involves the apparition of a lady in green who manifests herself at intervals around the grounds of St. Michael's and mysteriously follows the passing stranger. I wonder is she still searching vainly through the night for a lost loved one whose untimely death she was unable to accept. Her dress is green, a colour associated with tears and weeping, a colour appertaining to grief and to sorrow. I wonder if this apparition is persecuted by a love too deep to lie sleeping, by a loss too great to know the sanctions of rest. Must she forever follow the passing stranger in the hope that it is the one she so tragically lost all those years ago? So, if one night you are walking in the vicinity of St. Michael's and you are alone—but, perhaps, you are not alone—pause for thought and a little sadness before, pulling up your collar to keep out the chill, you hurry on your way through the dark to the welcome glow and the inexplicable joy of that light in the window.

The other ghostly resident at Aughton is a little more interesting for he, poor fellow, is burdened with the office of chains. He must have been clanking down the lonely lanes of St. Michael's for hundreds of years, although he has not been heard in recent times, or has he? Unfortunately we have no information as to his identity and we may speculate that he was a political prisoner who, when troops had been called to muster against the Spanish Armada on Aughton Moss in 1585, had deserted his post and relinquished his duty to sovereign and country. He may have been a prisoner taken when Cromwell fought a battle at Aughton with 4,000 men. He may have been a victim of the Press gang who came here in 1747. Supposition is an extravagant fellow but I feel such possibilities more pliable than merely classifying him as a petty criminal who, I feel sure, would not warrant the close proximity of chains. Is this clanking apparition trying to inform us of some long ago misdemeanour performed upon his person, an act of injustice, causing suffering and eventual death to its innocent victim? Indeed, history is littered with such crooked tales and so therefore we must be thankful that the injunctions of the law have improved favourably to become the honourable institutions of fairness, order and equality that we recognise today. We would do well to remember, when we hear the clanking of those chains one starry night, straining like an echo from the past, the times in our history when all was not so well.

Earlier we talked of superstitions and it was this very element prevalent in society and born, seemingly, as an absurd instinct within each propagating generation, that eventually led to the discontinuation of one of Aughton's most enjoyable innovations, her race-course.

Aughton race-course was every bit as popular and grand as her neighbour at Aintree and, likewise, was always well attended. The locals went to great lengths erecting stalls to accommodate all manner of delicacies. The sporting gentry arrived, the men wearing their amateur riding silks, to add a splash of colour to the occasion and were always mounted on horses of the most important order. The usual activities accompanying such events were pursued and throughout the day many hundreds of pounds changing hands found their way into the bookies' pockets. High class horses sweated and floundered over the hawthorns, stone walls and open ditches, leaving their disappointed owners to count the cost and foot the bills. The locals thoroughly enjoyed themselves and many had to be helped down the winding lanes to the sanctuary of their cottage homes. Drinking, merriment and high spirits ruled the day but, strangely it seems, the people of Aughton shared a troubled conscience concerning their day at the races. Somehow it did not seem respectable. In 1815, on the very day of the meeting, a terrible thunderstorm occurred which did great damage to the stalls and stands, leaving a trail of frightening devastation. The residents took this to be a sign, a judgement from God because of the accumulation of wickedness existing at these meetings. The result of this tempestous storm was to so upset the people that the 1815 race meeting at Aughton proved to be the last ever seen there. The superstitious folk decided it was more in their favour to keep to the straight and narrow road than to cross the wrath of their God.

> If you want to go where the best folk go
> Follow the road to Aughton
> By haunted road and high hedge row
> Follow the road to Aughton
>
> If you want to stay as young as you are
> Follow the road to Aughton
> Maybe you'll find that secret elixir
> If you follow the road to Aughton
>
> If you want to tread where a martyr trod
> Follow the road to Aughton
> Where they mustered troops on this green clod
> Follow the road to Aughton
>
> If you want to sit in an old church pew
> Follow the road to Aughton
> Where once the dogs, in prayer, sat too
> Follow the road to Aughton
>
> Come where they used the first umbrella
> Follow the road to Aughton
> By clergymen in stormy weather
> Just follow the road to Aughton
>
> If you want to see twelve Angels fair
> Follow the road to Aughton
> You might find more than Angels there
> If you follow the road to Aughton

The Legend of the Water Lilies

IN the Halsall, Shirdley Hill and Parbold districts of Lancashire there is an abundance of small, round ponds. Some have been filled in, but several still remain to cluster in the lonely fields and enhance the beauty of the wild landscape. To the local folk these ponds were known as the pits and were believed to date from ancient times.

The local story maintains that the pits were dug long ago for the purpose of putting Marley clay into the soil to enrich its fertility and its growing power. A more recent theory relates that the pits where the homes of an ancient people living in this area. During excavations of similar pits at Winchester they were found to have been roofed over with wattle and daub and used as dwelling places. It is quite possible the same explanation could apply to the pits in Lancashire.

There is a lane in the vicinity of Halsall called Renacres Lane, and in one of its fields lies such a pond. The pond is unusual for several reasons. Firstly, it has a repution for never freezing over, not even during the coldest of wintry weather. Secondly, at certain times of the year the surface of the pond is completely covered with the most astonishing display of water lilies. Thirdly, its contours trace the exact shape of a harp. Fourthly, it is the subject of a quaint and colourful local story.

In ancient times there came to Halsall a penniless traveller called Ranulph. He brought with him some friends and followers and they settled in this area. Ranulph was a wise and just man who won the affection of the local folk, so much so that they decided to make him their king. The area then became known as Ranulph's acres. Ranulph married a local girl and soon became the father of a beautiful daughter. The subject of her beauty was the most talked of thing in the land and people travelled daily to gaze on the wonder of it. Ranulph was a proud man and he had an ambitious idea. He ordered a pond to be built in the grounds of his palace; it was fashioned in the shape of a harp and into it he had placed the magical waters of an enchanted stream. The pond was to be a mirror to hold the reflection of his beautiful daughter.

Quite common at this time in our history were those pitiful creatures called witches. Not surprisingly, then, a witch lived within the vicinity of Ranulph's acres; moreover, she was a very jealous witch. Hagbah was old, ugly and mis-shapen and had two daughters of her own. Fate had been unkind to the old witch for her daughters were as unlovely as

61

she herself was. Hagbah was relentlessly bitter; she sat day in, day out in the top-most branch of a weather-worn, bent old tree overlooking the palace gardens and openly seethed with discontent. She watched the making of the pond and she saw the reflection of the princess in the magic of its silvery waters, and in uncontrollable anger she kicked the knobbly old tree. The tree shook and groaned so much that Hagbah's two daughters came running, crying, 'What ails you oh lovely ugly mother?'

'A wicked curse, a wicked curse,' she held her head and wailed, 'look at the reflection of the beautiful princess in the waters of the magical pond.'

'We see, we see,' hissed the two daughters as one.

'It should be you, my two fledglings, the monstrous products of my womb and I am very wretched. A curse on that nasty pond, a curse on that nasty princess, a curse for each knob on the branches of this knobbly old tree.'

As Hagbah cursed aloud the sky darkened and she turned herself into a cloud. She sped down on the pond in the palace gardens, blocking out the friendly sun and caused an evil blackness to fall upon the earth. Her daughters became the raging wind whose eerie song ran amock wrestling in the corners of the besieged garden. But the pond remained undisturbed, her waters calm and the reflection of the princess was safe within its keeping. Hagbah returned to brood in the confines of her old tree. 'You may as well touch the ceiling of the sky as cast an evil spell on this enchanted princess,' the old dame whined and puffed hard on her bent clay pipe.

As a matter of course a handsome young prince came to Ranulph's Acres, travelling many miles to gaze on the surface of the pond. As expected he too fell madly in love with the reflection he found there. Hagbah however had slyly watched the antics of the young prince and was most damnably angry. She ranted and raved, jumped up and down and the old tree heaved and sighed under the strain. 'A wicked curse, a wicked curse,' she screamed, 'a wicked curse for every knob of every branch of this knobbly tree'.

The witch cast her spell on the surface of the magical pond and made of it a witch mirror. The prince could no longer see the reflection of the princess but only the image of himself reflected in the glass. Hagbah turned her daughters into a flock of white swans and they flew down to the pond to gaze at their newly found beauty. As the birds touched the surface of the waters the witch glass shattered into a thousand thousand pieces and the flock of birds were transformed into water lilies of the purest white. The lilies completely covered the surface of the enchanted pond and the prince could not see the reflection of the princess. The prince dived into the waters of the pond and, in so doing, cut himself on the shattered witch glass. A drop of his blood found itself into the middle of each water lily forever staining its centre red.

As the waters covered the prince his wounds were healed, he found the princess and they remain happily together, even to this day, in the sanctuary of that harp-shaped pond in Renacres Lane. Hagbah has her wish too for her daughters dwell eternally on the surface of the pond in the form of water lilies. They remain forever as prisoners within the beauty of these breath-taking plants, forever to be admired by the passing stranger, by you and by me.

Did you hear the water lilies stir
A little sigh, a murmur here and there
What said the wind to Autumn as he stripped her bare?

Ranulph's lands are singing sweetly, low
To Ranulph's golden acres I must go
To place a cloak of 'waking where the water lilies grow

To linger where the Willow bends and sighs
As ever on the naked hour, it cries
A story to the restless nomads of the skies

    A curse, a curse, the old witch cried.

A garden nestles snugly on the plains
Is touched by dew and early morning rains
There the merry Mavis sits and sings its last refrains

And here a Royal maiden sleeps
The sun is set, the shadow creeps
As on the distant hill, a witch in anguish, weeps

For here a magic pond is found
A very harp shape in the ground
It keeps the Royal image ever safe and sound

    A curse, a curse, the old witch cried.

Come rain, come snow, come hail
You'll hear the 'crepid witch one wail
But the curse is lost in raging wind and is of no avail

Turn, turn, the witch is a cloud
Her daughters become wind, wailing, loud
They cast over the garden a wicked death shroud

But the magical pond is not disturbed
Where the beautiful Princess is safely interred
And 'neath its silvery waters her laughter is heard

    A curse, a curse, the old witch cried.

The witch is astride her old oak tree
Her two daughters together, they sit, all three
As ugly as only three witches could be

Jealousy smoulders within each breast
Together they have but one sole quest
To destroy the beauty of the Royal Princess

But along came a Prince, handsome, grand
Came seeking the Princess in Ranulph's land
And he brought her fine jewels for her neck and her hand

    A curse, a curse, the old witch cried.

The old witch ranted, the old witch raved
This Prince for her daughters she wanted and craved
And now for this purpose a sly trick she played

A curse, a curse, she sang to the rain
And the magical pond a witch mirror became
The image of the Princess was lost in depth and ne'er seen again

Turn, turn, my daughters she said
And as a flock of swans to the pond they sped
To bask in their beauty, in vainess were led

    A curse, a curse, the old witch cried.

As the swans touched the surface of the magical pond
They were changed on the instant by a magical wand
To Water Lilies, and so at last, the beauty for which they had longed

Now into the water the Prince dived true
Smashing the mirror and passing through
And so in this magical harp shaped pond the love of the Prince
                    and the Princess grew

But, on smashing the witch glass, the Prince sorely bled
And 'though he was healed by the waters, 'tis said
His blood stained the heart of the Water Lily quite quite red

    A curse, a curse, the old witch cried.

Did you hear the Water Lilies stir
A little sigh, a murmur here and there
What said the wind to Autumn as he stripped her bare?